Piano Exam Pieces

ABRSM Grade 3

Selected from the 2019 & 2020 syllabus

C000258629

Name

Date of exam

Contents

Editor for ABRSM: Richard Jones

Other pieces for Grade 3

First published in 2018 by ABRSM (Publishing) Ltd, a wholly owned subsidiary of ABRSM, 4 London Wall Place, London EC2Y 5AU, United Kingdom
© 2018 by The Associated Board of the Royal Schools of Music
Distributed worldwide by Oxford University Press

Music origination by Julia Bovee
Cover by Kate Benjamin & Andy Potts, with thanks to Brighton College
Printed in England by Halstan & Co. Ltd, Amersham, Bucks., on materials from sustainable sources.
Reprinted in 2018

Allegro

First movement from Sonatina in F, Op. 12 No. 3

James Hook
(1746–1827)

This lively, energetic piece is selected from a set of 12 Sonatinas that Hook wrote for his piano pupils. It is designed in rounded binary form – that is, A B A (bb. 1, 9, 21).

The English musician James Hook was gifted as a child, both at the keyboard and in composition. Most of his adult life was spent in London as organist at the Marylebone and Vauxhall pleasure gardens – parks in which people could stroll to the accompaniment of music.

Source: *Twelve Sonatinos* [sic] *for the Harpsichord or Piano-Forte for the use of Scholars, Op. 12* (London, *c*.1776). All dynamics and slurs are editorial suggestions only.

© 1984 by The Associated Board of the Royal Schools of Music
Adapted from Hook: *Twelve Sonatinas*, Op. 12, edited by Lionel Salter (ABRSM)

Giga

Second movement from Sonata in D minor

A:2

Carlos de Seixas
(1704–42)

Carlos de Seixas was a virtuoso on the organ and harpsichord, and became the leading Portuguese keyboard composer of the early 18th century. At the age of only 14 he succeeded his father as organist of Coimbra Cathedral. He moved to Lisbon in 1720 and became organist of the Royal Chapel, a post he held for the rest of his life.

In the Baroque period, the giga was the Italian version of the gigue – fast and lively, with even quavers in compound time. This giga changes mood several times from forceful to gentle and back to forceful, as reflected in the dynamics.

Source: Lisboa, Biblioteca do Palácio Nacional da Ajuda, Mus.MS 48-I-2. The following accidentals are missing in the source and have been added by the editor: b. 8, ♮; b. 11, first ♯; b. 19, ♮. The rest in b. 12 is also editorial. The first bass note of b. 22 reads f in the source, but has been corrected here to a. The last chord has been corrected by the editor from dotted crotchet to dotted minim. All dynamics and slurs are editorial suggestions only.

© 2018 by The Associated Board of the Royal Schools of Music

Bransle de la torche

from *Terpsichore*

Arranged by Robert Pell

Michael Praetorius
(1571–1621)

Michael Praetorius was one of the most versatile and prolific German composers of his day. Most of his works are sacred, but he also published one major secular work – a set of instrumental dances called *Terpsichore*, published in 1612.

In the Renaissance period, the branle (or bransle) was a popular French dance for groups of people. The movement of the feet can be heard in the characteristic repeated notes in the second half of each bar (bb. 1–3 etc.). The piece is written in binary form (A B, bb. 1 and 17) with varied repeats, starting at bb. 9 and 25. It is written in the old Dorian mode – like D minor, but without the key signature.

Reproduced from *Piano Mix 3*, compiled and edited by David Blackwell (ABRSM)

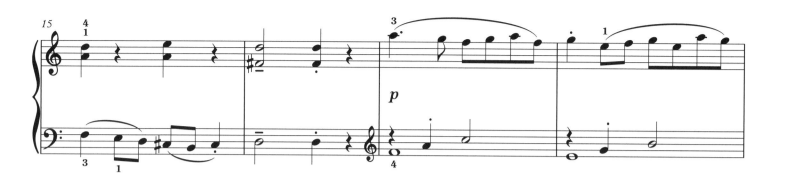

Shadows

No. 3 from *River and Rainbow*

Walter Carroll
(1869–1955)

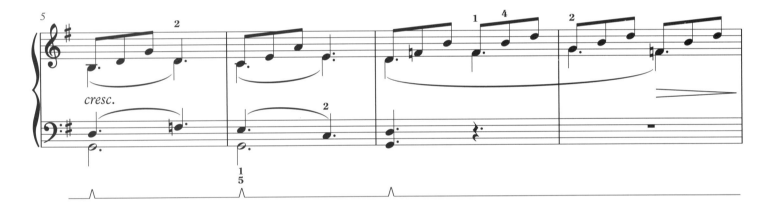

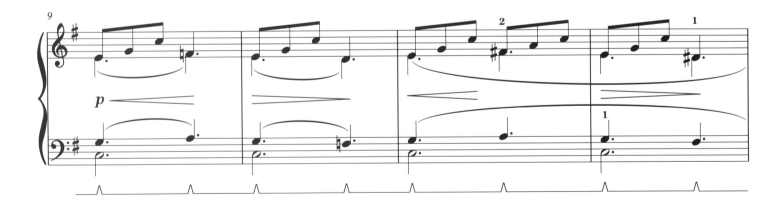

Walter Carroll was born in Manchester and played a significant role in the musical life of the city, teaching at the Royal Manchester College of Music and at Manchester University, and acting as music adviser to the local education authority. He wrote many piano pieces for students, including *River and Rainbow*, a set of ten miniatures with programmatic titles.

The third piece from this collection, 'Shadows', is prefaced by a motto: 'Only the night air, and the dream;/Only the far, sweet-smelling wave.' It is a night piece, then, describing Carroll's impressions of a place where the river flows into the sea, hence the swaying motion of the music. Note that the melody lies in the right-hand dotted crotchets that sustain the lowest note of the broken chords.

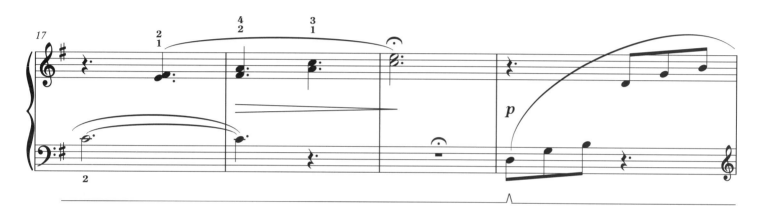

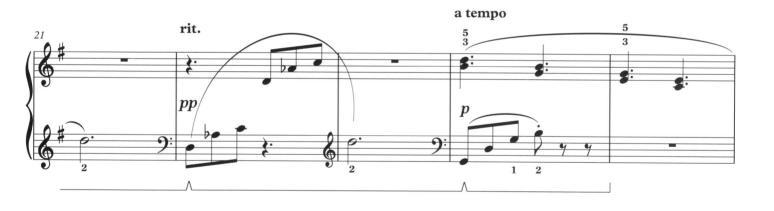

Allegretto grazioso

No. 11 from *Kleine Blumen*, Op. 205

Cornelius Gurlitt
(1820–1901)

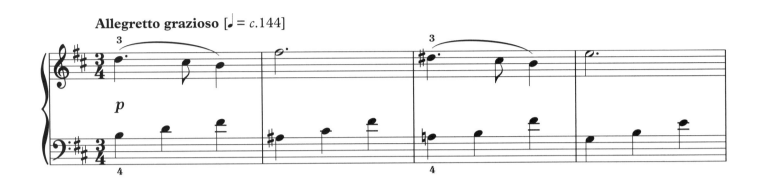

Cornelius Gurlitt was born in Germany, near Hamburg, and studied music in Copenhagen. Later he became organist of Altona Cathedral and professor of music at the Hamburg Conservatory.

He composed over 200 works, including many small, attractive pieces for young people, which often take the form of character-pieces, descriptive of particular moods or scenes. Gurlitt's fondness for musical description explains why the collection from which 'Allegretto grazioso' has been selected is entitled *Kleine Blumen* (Little Flowers). The piece is in ternary form (ABA[1]), with a haunting, dance-like A section in B minor, a contrasting B section in F sharp major (b. 17), followed by an abridged return of A (b. 25).

Source: *Kleine Blumen. 12 leichte…Tonstücke für das Pianoforte. Op. 205* (London: Augener & Co., 1894)

Prelude

First movement from Serenade in C, Op. 183 No. 1

Carl Reinecke
(1824–1910)

B:3

espressivo

The German composer and pianist Carl Reinecke worked in Germany and Scandinavia. In the late 19th century he settled in Leipzig as professor (later director) of the conservatory and conductor of the Gewandhaus Orchestra.

Reinecke's piano music includes many pieces for young people, such as the *Fünf Serenaden für die Jugend* (Five Serenades for the Young), Op. 183, from which this movement is selected. The style of this prelude, with its constant arpeggiated chords, is very similar to earlier examples by Bach and Schumann. Here, the main melody lies at the top of the right-hand arpeggiated chords, then moves to the left hand in the middle section (bb. 9–16).

Source: *Fünf Clavier-Serenaden für die Jugend, Op. 183* (Leipzig, 1885)

un poco slentando   a tempo

C:1

Dance

No. 8 from *For Children*, Vol. 2

Béla Bartók
(1881–1945)

The Hungarian composer Béla Bartók wrote *For Children* between 1908 and 1910. It was his first large collection of folksong arrangements and contains both Hungarian and Slovakian tunes. The composer's aim was to reveal 'the simple and non-Romantic beauties of folk music' to young pianists. He revised the collection in 1943.

'Dance' is selected from Volume 2 of the revised version, which is based on Slovakian folk tunes. In this piece, the folk melody is played three times (bb. 5, 13 and 23), each time with a different chordal accompaniment.

© Copyright 1946 by Boosey & Hawkes, Inc., New York/Editio Musica Budapest
Reproduced from *For Children*, Volume 2 (ISMN 979-0-060-112317)

Diversion

No. 1 from *Diversions*

Richard Rodney Bennett
(1936–2012)

Richard Rodney Bennett was an English composer who studied at the Royal Academy of Music, London, with Howard Ferguson and Lennox Berkeley. Later he had lessons in Paris with Pierre Boulez. He was also a jazz pianist, and his strong interest in jazz often influenced his compositions.

The first of Bennett's *Diversions*, selected here, is a playful piece that darkens in flat keys (bb. 8–14), then brightens as sharp keys return (bb. 15–25). This central 'diversion' is preceded and followed by the main theme (bb. 1 and 26), giving the piece an overall arch shape (ABA[1]). The composer's metronome mark is ♩. = 80, but students might prefer a more relaxed tempo of ♩. = *c*.72.

C:3

Blues in the Attic

Nikki Iles
(born 1963)

As a blues piece, this is rather melancholic in tone, but with pungent dissonances and funky rhythms. The middle section (bb. 10–16) is built on a chain of fifths in the bass. It is followed by a slightly varied reprise of the opening section (b. 17) plus a coda (b. 26).

Nikki Iles is a well-known English jazz pianist and composer who has worked with many leading jazz musicians. She is also active in the field of jazz education, teaching this type of music at Middlesex University and at the Royal Academy of Music, London.